On a Snowy Day

by Cindy Peattie

What do you see?

I see the snow.

What do you see?

I see the trees.

What do you see?

I see the shovel.

What do you see?

I see the plow.

What do you see?

I see the hill.

What do you see?

I see the sled.

What do you see?

I see the snowballs.

What **do** you see?